Gentle Little Lion

Claude Clément
Adapted by Patricia Jensen
Illustrations by Marcelle Geneste

Reader's Digest Kids
Pleasantville, N.Y.—Montreal

Little Lion was a gentle cub who lived on a savanna, deep in the heart of Africa. He spent his days romping in the grass and napping in the sun.

When Little Lion's friends played rough games, he didn't join in. Little Lion didn't like roaring contests, make-believe battles, or wrestling matches.

One day, the lions were going off to hunt.
"Come along," Little Lion's father said.
"You must learn to hunt. Then you'll be able
to take care of yourself, and later on you
will be able to protect your family, too."

"I don't want to hunt," said Little Lion. "It's too rough. Why can't I just stay here and play?"

Father Lion looked stern. "It's time for you to begin acting like a lion. Now, please come along."

And so Little Lion walked along behind the other lions.

As he walked, Little Lion worried and
wondered, "Will I ever learn to take care
of myself? Will I ever act like a lion?
I only know I don't want to hunt right now."
    While the other lions hurried ahead,
Little Lion slipped away. He ran and ran
until he came to some trees.

Little Lion heard a rustling sound. He looked up and saw a frightened zebra.

"Help!" gasped the zebra. "Lions!" He turned to run away.

"Wait!" cried Little Lion. "Don't be afraid. I'm all alone, and I'd really like to play with you."

Little Lion followed the zebra into a clearing. There he met all of the zebra's friends. He romped in the grass with the elephants and gave a playful monkey a ride on his back.

"I've never had so much fun!" Little Lion said.

The animals played so hard and so long that they became sleepy. Soon they all lay down in the warm sun to take a nap.

Meanwhile, Father Lion had been searching
all across the savanna for his son. Finally,
he came upon Little Lion, fast asleep.

"What a naughty cub," thought Father Lion.
"First he runs away. Now he's sleeping in the

tall grass while all the other lions are worrying about him. When will he learn to grow up and act like a lion?"

Father Lion became so angry that he suddenly roared a very loud, long roar.

Little Lion jumped up—and so did all his new friends. They took one look at Father Lion and started running as fast as they could. This made Little Lion angry. Why had his father frightened his friends? Suddenly Little Lion roared, too—a very loud, long roar.

Just as suddenly, both Little Lion and his father were quiet. They stared at each other, and then they began to laugh.

"I can roar!" said Little Lion.

"You certainly can!" said his father. "And lions who roar the way you do will be able to take care of themselves and protect their families, too!"

Little Lion was so happy that he leaped into the air. "I can roar!" he shouted.

From then on, Little Lion was allowed to play with the other animals. Every day they played games in the grass and napped in the warm sun. Father Lion stopped worrying about his son acting like a lion and being able to take care of himself. And Little Lion didn't worry about it either.

The Lion belongs to the cat family, which includes tigers, leopards, jaguars, cheetahs, and house cats. Lions are the second largest of all cats. Tigers are the largest.

Lions often live in groups of 10 to 25. These groups are called prides. Male lions protect the pride and its territory. Female lions do most of the hunting and look after the young.

Lions cannot run very fast for long distances. They hunt by sneaking up on other animals. Lions often hunt at night because they can surprise their prey more easily in the dark.